PENGUIN BOOKS

HOT

Michael Leunig's words and pictures
were first published in Australia in 1965.
He was born in Melbourne and now
lives on a farm in north-eastern Victoria.

Hot comprises pieces that have previously
appeared in the Melbourne *Age* and the
Sydney Morning Herald.

ALSO BY MICHAEL LEUNIG

Michael Leunig

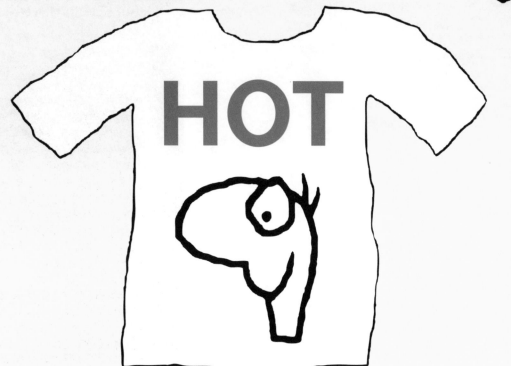

HOT

...and bothered

PENGUIN BOOKS

PENGUIN BOOKS

Published by the Penguin Group
Penguin Group (Australia)
250 Camberwell Road, Camberwell, Victoria 3124, Australia
(a division of Pearson Australia Group Pty Ltd)
Penguin Group (USA) Inc.
375 Hudson Street, New York, New York 10014, USA
Penguin Group (Canada)
90 Eglinton Avenue East, Suite 700, Toronto, Canada ON M4P 2Y3
(a division of Pearson Penguin Canada Inc.)
Penguin Books Ltd
80 Strand, London WC2R 0RL England
Penguin Ireland
25 St Stephen's Green, Dublin 2, Ireland
(a division of Penguin Books Ltd)
Penguin Books India Pvt Ltd
11 Community Centre, Panchsheel Park, New Delhi – 110 017, India
Penguin Group (NZ)
67 Apollo Drive, Rosedale, North Shore 0632, New Zealand
(a division of Pearson New Zealand Ltd)
Penguin Books (South Africa) (Pty) Ltd
24 Sturdee Avenue, Rosebank, Johannesburg 2196, South Africa

Penguin Books Ltd, Registered Offices: 80 Strand, London, WC2R 0RL, England

First published by Penguin Group (Australia), 2007

10 9 8 7 6 5 4 3 2 1

Text and illustrations copyright © Michael Leunig 2007

The moral right of the author has been asserted

Design by George Dale © Penguin Group (Australia)
Printed and bound in Australia by
McPherson's Printing Group, Maryborough, Victoria

National Library of Australia
Cataloguing-in-Publication data:

Leunig, Michael, 1945– .
Hot.
ISBN 978 0 14 300797 5 (pbk.).
1. Caricatures and cartoons – Australia. 2. Australian wit and humor, Pictorial.
I. Title.

741.5994

penguin.com.au

Glossary of characters and concepts in this book

AL QAEDA The bad guys in the famous television series *Get Smart*, featuring secret agent Maxwell Smart

AUSSIE A light-hearted Australian

AUSTRALIAN VALUES Vague, unspecified qualities. Whatever

BANANA A soft, curved yellow thing

BODY PARTS Essential ingredients in advertising and the film industry

CAMOMILE A flower used for calming people who are being driven around the twist by the new global economy

COLLINGWOOD SUPPORTER A naïve, forlorn and tragic individual who supports the Collingwood Football Club and believes that the earth is flat and that they will win the lottery one day

DAVID HICKS A political prisoner

THE DEVIL The nation's largest employer and most popular motivational speaker, psychotherapist and life coach

EXIT STRATEGY Polite name for either a nervous breakdown or a getaway car after a robbery

EXPLOSION A means of getting what we want. A disturbance that happens repeatedly in the internal combustion engine, causing millions of people to go whizzing about all over the place at great speed with delusions of grandeur

FEDERAL POLICE No definition currently
available
FISHNET STOCKINGS Undergarment worn
by the Minister for Foreign Affairs
FOX TERRIER A white dog with black or
brown patches and a mind of its own
GLOBAL WARMING A new umbrella anxiety
that displaces previous fears about dust mites,
terrorists and cancer
HAPPINESS A state which is bad for the
economy and must be disabled before it gets
out of control
JOHN HOWARD (pictured here) A wave-riding
Australian prime minister who tragically mistook
the force of the wave for his own personal power
KYLIE A female entertainer yearning for love
LEAVES Green bits that hang from tree branches
and provide shade and oxygen for humans
LIFE A frightening prospect which must be
subdued at all costs

LOWEST APPETITES The matter upon
which democracy hinges
LUST A human impulse which gives meaning
to life in Western society and acts as the principle
social and economic glue
LYING RODENT A political candidate, a media
executive, 'a nice bloke'
PETROL A magic potion
PROSPERITY An orgy of immense vulgarity
and stupidity
QUEEN No definition currently available
RAIN DANCE A dance usually performed in
public by a nude crowd who want relief from the
drought and relief from clothing and social norms
SHED A domestic corrugated-iron building where
married men brood and listen to the football
on old radio sets
SURGE Military masturbation
TERROR An awful feeling induced by the media,
soldiers, politicians, bushfires and parents
VIOLENCE A military science. Social and
economic glue that ensures the flow of petrol
at affordable prices. Traditional Australian
recreational activity
VOID A popular destination
WAR A time when so much is inflicted
on so many by so few
WARMONGER A newspaper columnist.
An editor. A talkback host

HOW TO KEEP YOUR DIGNITY IN A CRASS AND VULGAR WORLD.

True dignity comes from integrity.

Integrity is a garden.

your dignity can be kept in a small, simple ceramic bowl.

The bowl can be kept in a quiet place in the garden.

If the bowl fills with rainwater or a bird tips it over — so much the better.

Leunig

THE DUST BATH — another water saving strategy.

DON'T SNEER AT THE COMMON DUST BATH; YOU MIGHT BE HAVING ONE SOONER THAN YOU THINK.

A LONG, SLOW, NUDE DUST BATH ON A SUNNY AFTERNOON CAN BE A SENSUOUS AND EROTIC EXPERIENCE FOR COURTING COUPLES.

CHICKENS AND SPARROWS HAVE LONG KNOWN THE PLEASURE AND THERAPEUTIC VALUE OF THE DUST BATH.

BE CAREFUL ON WINDY DAYS; CLOUDS OF DUST ARISING FROM YOUR BACK YARD CAN CREATE BAD FEELINGS IN THE NEIGHBOURHOOD

NAKED IS THE WAY TO GO, AND VIGOROUS TUMBLING AND FLIP-FLOPPING ABOUT IS THE RECOMMENDED ACTION.

WE MAY WELL BE RUNNING OUT OF WATER BUT WE ARE RICH IN DUST.

Leunig

The SEVEN WONDERS of the WEEKend.

I wonder where my keys are...

I wonder why you can't keep them in a safe place.

I wonder if I should be living with this woman.

Exclusive interview with Trackie Daks, the Prime Minister's famous tracksuit pants.

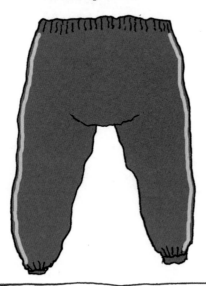

Trackie Daks, you've been close to the Prime Minister now for eleven years; what's it been like for you – how do you feel now that it's all coming to an end?

T.D. Well yes, we've been very close and I've seen a side of the Prime Minister that nobody else knows about – a softer more vulnerable side I guess. I've had a special view from the inside and it's been quite amazing. I've experienced some dark stuff too. But I feel very sad – and that's probably why I look so sad.

Trackie Daks, everyone in Australia has come to know you by your loveable, relaxed, green and gold good looks, but we can't help wonder what goes on inside you. If we could look inside Trackie Daks, what would we see?

T.D. My interior life has been very interesting. I've had a lot of strange stuff to deal with but I also have a soft, warm and forgiving soul.

You mentioned "dark stuff". Can you

be more specific?

T.D. That was something between me and the Prime Minister. That's all I can say.

The polls have been running strongly against the Prime Minister – do you feel any responsibility?

T.D. I can honestly tell you that I have no regrets or shame about my role. I have done everything I could do. My elastic is as twangy and snappy and tight now as it ever was – the problem is that the elastic out there in the electorate seems to be sagging and slackening off – and that's a total mystery.

And finally Trackie Daks, your thoughts about retirement?

Well, there's some talk about me going into a glass case in the National Museum – I don't know; but I can tell you this for sure: there'll be no more ironing and starching every morning at five a.m. – no way mate!

Leunig

HILL-BILLY DROUGHT SONG

On a dried-up rustic hill I heard a banjo ringing;

A yokel with a moonshine still sat with his wife a' singing

"We're making water out of booze So's we can have a shower;

So buckle on them dancin' shoes my pretty little flower."

RAINMAKING OPTIONS AND CHANCES OF SUCCESS

NUDE RAIN DANCE.
15%

PRAYER
15%

DUCK EMPATHY
57%

NUDE PRAYER
WITH DUCK
87.5%

Leunig

GLOBAL WARMING

IT IS TIME TO
LEARN THE GREAT
ART OF CHEERFUL
SADNESS.

THIS IS MEDITATION
THIS IS YOGA
THIS IS PRAYER

DOGS CAN SHOW
YOU HOW IT'S DONE.
DUCKS ALSO.

CHECK YOUR REFLECTION
IN A PUDDLE. YOU WILL
SEE THE SWEET, HEARTBREAKING
FOOLISHNESS IN YOUR EYES
AND IN YOUR SMILE.

EMPATHISE WITH
THEM · STARE INTO
THEIR EYES.
CHEERFUL SADNESS WILL
BEGIN TO FLOW.

WHAT YOU TELL YOUR
GRANDCHILDREN WILL
NOT MATTER SO MUCH;
THEY WILL JUST STARE
INTO YOUR EYES
AND DREAM OF DUCKS
AND DOGS.
THIS WILL HELP A BIT...
... SURELY ?

Leunig

Let's have a barbecue!
We're already having one... and we're the sausages.
EARTH HEATING UP
Leunig

"Honey-pie, I'd like us to get into cleaner technology. I think you should wash the vehicle when we get home."

Do not dumb me,
Do not dumb me,
Do not dumb me down;
Dumb me upwards,
upwards to
The bigger end of town.

Dumb me upwards,
Dumb me upwards,
Dumb me to the sky.
The greatest dumbness
in the world
Is where the big men fly.

Leunig

POLITICIANS ARE A
PRIMITIVE PEOPLE WHO
ARE ALWAYS FIGHTING
AND CAUSING TROUBLE.

THEY WON'T INTEGRATE INTO
NORMAL SOCIETY. IT'S NO USE
TRYING TO UNDERSTAND THEM —
THEY ARE NOMADIC OPPORTUNISTS.

THEY LOVE BOOZING AND
FORNICATING. THEY ARE
UNRELIABLE AND YOU
CAN'T TRUST THEM

GREAT SWAGS OF PUBLIC
MONEY AND RESOURCE HAVE
BEEN THROWN AT THEM BUT
THE SITUATION NEVER IMPROVES.
THEY WILL ALWAYS BE A
BIG HEADACHE.

Leunig

ALL OPTIONS ARE ON THE TABLE.

Leunig

Reverse-Psychotherapy

Why would you want to be sane in a mad world? It will only cause you misery.

It's better to go mad – it's easier, and who knows, you could become powerful and influential.

Reverse psychotherapy can help you overcome this terrible block – this burden, this liability, quaintly known as sanity.

Television, radio and newspapers can also be cheap, effective and readily available forms of reverse-psychotherapy.

You'll start to enjoy life again — the wars, the invasions; the justifications — they'll all seem normal, necessary and mature.

But be careful; bitter and twisted is the madness you need. Avoid dotty — it's for losers.

Leunig

The First Day of School. (A SONG) ♪♪♪♪

The first day of school could not have been merrier;
The teacher turned out to be a fox terrier
Who taught us to leap and taught us to bark
And chase little birdies all over the park.
For the rest of our lives we still had the spark
From the wonderful first day of school.

WHEN AND BY WHOM WERE THE FOLLOWING WORDS SPOKEN, "HE WHO CONTROLS THE PAST, CONTROLS THE FUTURE" and "HISTORY IS WRITTEN BY THE WINNERS."?

I HAVEN'T GOT A BLOODY CLUE SIR.

DOLT! DUNCE! YOU'RE TELLING ME YOU DON'T UNDERSTAND ONE OF THE MOST SACRED PRINCIPLES OF WESTERN CIVILIZATION..?! YOU'RE AN IMBECILE!

NO I'M NOT SIR I'M A COLLINGWOOD SUPPORTER SIR.

Leunig

Getting
YOUR LIFE
in
ORDER

The FLOOR is
not a CLOSET.

The CLOSET is
not a place to
Live your life.

YOUR LIFE is
not SUCH a
MESS.

YOUR MESS is
on the FLOOR

The FLOOR is
not a CLOSET.

Leunig

Scientists Discover "Lost World"

SCIENTISTS DISCOVER
"LOST WORLD",
LOVELY WORLD,
WORLD OF WISDOM.

BRIGHT, SIMPLE, NATURAL SPIRITS.
TRUTHFUL PEOPLE, MUSICAL PEOPLE;
LOVELY, LOVELY, LOVELY CREATURES

GENTLE SOULS, GLORIOUS PEOPLE,
HUMBLE, PEACEFUL, LOVING PEOPLE.
SWEETHEARTS, EVERY ONE.

SCIENTISTS DISCOVER "LOST WORLD".
SCIENTISTS MAKE SECRET PACT.
SCIENTISTS TURN AND WALK AWAY.
AWAY. AWAY. AWAY. AWAY.

Leunig

...excuse me
I want to make
a joke please...

HAVE YOU FILLED IN
THE NECESSARY
PAPER-WORK?

yes.

HAVE YOU GOT THE
SPECIAL INSURANCE
AND HAD THE
MEDICAL CHECKUP?

I have.

ALRIGHT THEN.
MAKE YOUR
JOKE.

..hell,
I can't
remember it.

THERE'S A FIVE
THOUSAND DOLLAR
PENALTY FOR
THAT.

I haven't
got any
money

THREE WEEKS IN
SOLITARY AND A
HUNDRED LASHES.
....
......

NEXT!

Leunig

SEVEN
TYPES
of
ORdinary
HAPPINESS

SECRET HAPPINESS
WHICH IS STEADY
BUT BEAUTIFULLY
DELICATE

Three minutes of
happiness borrowed
from a dog.

TRADITIONAL
LYING DOWN
HAPPINESS

The happiness which comes from staring at a rock.

HAPPINESS BLENDED WITH A MYSTERIOUS SADNESS

The strange happiness associated with seeing a meteorite or shooting star.

Diffuse, residual happiness resulting from rhythmic domestic tasks such as washing the dishes.

Leunig

Christmas is coming
The goose is getting sad.

So is Mum
And so is Dad.

Under the tree
Lie Santa's
presents:

Two little packets
Of anti-depressants.

Leunig

Once upon a time there was a boofhead....

... who married an airhead

They had two little dickheads...

... and lived happily ever after – not a problem.

<u>END OF STORY</u>.

Leunig

HERE IS
THE NEWS

and here are
the buckets!

Leunig

Maybe the rich people
should be paid in food
vouchers to stop them
wrecking the world.

Maybe everybody
should be paid in
psychotherapy
vouchers...

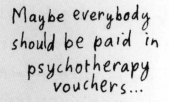

Leunig

STOLEN PARTS

Oh where did you get those rose red lips,
So full and ripe and sweet?
They're made with the tissue found in the tips
Of a dead man's stolen feet.

And if you kiss me, should I be scared
Of the dead man's cold, grey toes?
Have no fear of these lips so red,
There's worse things in my nose.

Leun

AUTUMN SPECIAL: SOME OLD LEAVES REVEAL THEIR SECRETS FOR A LONG LIFE.

" Work hard, do your photosynthesis daily and don't expect any congratulations"

" Unto thine own self be true."

" location, location "

" Better to have loved and lost than never to have loved at all "

" I loved the wind. I had a wonderful relationship with the wind. "

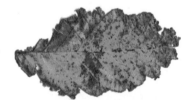

" on a warm summer night, rustle gently, rustle passionately and rustle often."

Leunig

... before we think about surgical removal we'll try putting you on camomile tea for a few weeks and see what happens.
Leunig

The art of wallowing is too much neglected yet it is such a profound, innocent and reliable pleasure...

Transfer lukewarm mixture to bathtub, remove clothing and begin wallowing.

... and such a sweet and noble means of knowing the soul's mysterious truth.

Roll slowly about in tapioca (sago) for 2-3 hours groaning occasionally with pleasure.

METHOD:
Take 20 KG. of tapioca (sago), soak overnight and simmer until sticky, gluggy consistency is achieved.

Now see how the world's depravity recedes from the heart. See how truth rushes in to fill the anxious, aching void.

Let the day go...WITH SAGO!

Leunig

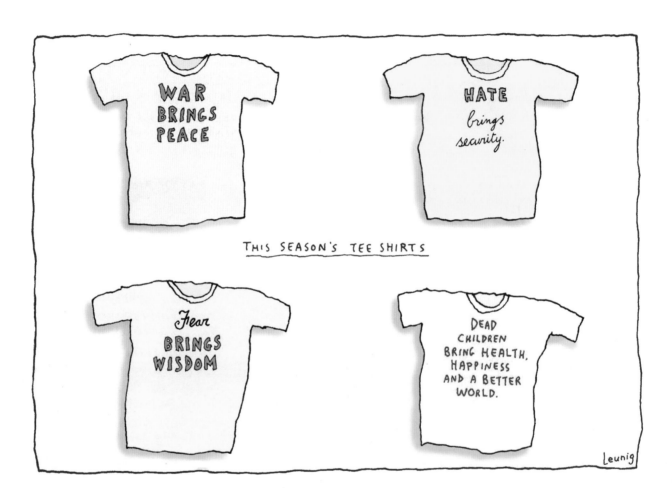

WHEN THE OIL RUNS OUT. Q+A.

Q. Maybe a donkey?
A. Certainly.

Q. Are donkeys much
trouble?
A. Compared to humans
they are very sweet.

Q. Do I have to stay on
the road?
A. No, you can ride your
donkey all over
the place.

Q. Will it be fun?
A. It will be such fun,
you'll love it.

Leunig

BY THEIR SIM CARDS, YE SHALL KNOW THEM.

You are your
SIM card and
your SIM card
is YOU

LEFT
Adam Receives
his SIM card.
from God

They were Australians.
He was a republican.
She was a monarchist.

They fell in love.
They got married.

They had two
beautiful children;

One was an anarchist;
The other was a fascist.

The household operated
as an anarchistic,
fascist, republican
monarchy.

At the end of the day
they called the system
"our joint", or "our place", and
sometimes "home, sweet home".

Leunig

THE "BLOKE BOOSTER" — A SHED FOR THE MODERN MAN.

NOW AT LAST, A SHED FOR THE MAN WHO LIVES IN A CITY APARTMENT.

BUILD YOUR OWN COFFEE-TABLE MINI-SHED WITH THIS D.I.Y. KIT WHICH INCLUDES MINI CORRUGATED IRON SHEETS, MINI STEEL FRAMING, MINI CONCRETE SLAB PLUS MINI WORK-BENCH AND MINI TOOL SHELVES WITH MINI AM-FM RADIO RECEIVER.

A SATISFIED CUSTOMER TELLS:

" I was confused, frustrated and depressed until my wife gave me a Bloke Booster mini-shed. I sit and stare at it and meditate and soon my troubles are gone. It's a safe haven for my soul and since I've been going into my shed, confidence has returned and I've started to whistle again. Things have improved between me and the wife too — and I can hold my head up because I built it myself. "

ACTUAL SIZE OF CORRUGATED IRON SHEETS (COLOURBOND, ZINCALUME OR GAL.)

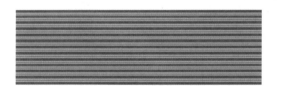

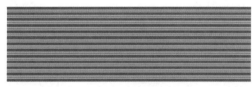

"AT LAST, I'VE GOT MY OWN SHED"

Leunig

THE CAR of the FUTURE

The car of the future will be chocolate powered.

FUTURE WARS WILL BE FOUGHT OVER CHOCOLATE BARS AND COCOA PLANTATIONS.

THE DRIVER WILL EAT THE CHOCOLATE WHICH WILL PROVIDE ENERGY TO OPERATE THE PEDAL MECHANISM.

Dark chocolate will be used to power racing cars and hooligan vehicles

SIMPLE PEDAL CARS HAVE LONG BEEN IN EXISTENCE AS CHILDREN'S TOYS BUT AT LAST THEIR TIME HAS TRULY COME.

DRIVERS OF THE FUTURE WILL HAVE PIMPLES AND BAD TEETH — AND MAGNIFICENT THIGHS!

Leunig

This is the seismic chart showing the nuclear explosion ..
... and this is a temperature chart about the earth getting hotter.
And this graph shows the deaths caused by current military conflicts
What's that little one there at the bottom?
That's just a speck of fly poo.
Oh how beautiful. Let's talk about the fly poo!
Leunig

THE TRADITIONAL NAKED RAIN DANCE

This old favourite is a vigorous, free-form unsynchronized dance, best performed by large groups in daylight hours accompanied by chanting and drumming and is not unlike the tarantella.

THE PRIDE OF ERIN

This old classic can prove troublesome on uneven ground – in a paddock etc. – and is not notably successful for bringing moisture or anything else very much, but worth a try.

THE BIG BANG

This is 100% guaranteed to bring rain. Another nude romp in a hornpipe/ho-down style, executed in a large public space, this reliable dance is a 12 hour marathon and can only be performed by four strictly specified people. The four dancers must be: the Prime Minister, the Attorney-General, the Treasurer and the Minister for Foreign Affairs. This will definitely bring relief to the nation.

THE NUDE SAMBA

This fascinating drought breaker is best performed naked under a full moon on a warm night by couples – but caution is advised because lightning and flooding may suddenly occur.

Leunig

Albert's a dual fuel person.
He's a petrol head during the
Grand Prix and an air head
for the rest of the year.

Leunig

I want to go to Curly beach
And ride the curly sea
And paddle out beyond the reach
Of those who'd straighten me

I'll take a little curly shell
And hold it to my ear
And when I hear the distant swell:
The gentle, distant magic bell,
I'll know the coast is clear.

Leunig

Rare Parrot Spotted after 130 years — ABC NEWS

The blue fronted fig parrot
has been spotted at last.
REJOICE

Yesterday the parrot held its first press conference.

what is
your message
for humanity?

Leunig

Come on dad, don't be such a boring old Mufti.
Now that we've got modernity, I'm perfectly
safe by myself, dressed like this, on the last
train home after the pub closes. I read all
about it in the newspaper. It's called freedom.

Leunig

WILD SCENES AT BRIGHTON HAT SHOP

Special forces riot police were unable to subdue a Toorak woman who is currently holding them at bay in a milliner's shop in Melbourne's south-eastern suburbs. The incident developed after Quarantine and Customs officials, acting on a bird-flu tipoff, attempted to seize a feather hat being made for Mrs. Pussington-Bigge of Toorak by her new milliner, Basil of Brighton. Capsicum spray and high-pressure fire hoses were no match for the wrath of the irate society matron who has taken refuge on the roof of the exclusive bayside boutique.

Last night, illuminated by police spotlights, a defiant Pussington-Bigge could be seen clutching the large, crumpled hat as she sat astride a gargoyle demanding to see her astrologer.

Basil of Brighton is believed to be under sedation and several special squad members have received counselling after being treated for shock and facial scratches.

A witness reports that the sounds coming from the shop were "awesome and electrifying". A reliable source from South Yarra is quoted as saying, "Don't worry, Pussington-Bigge will be at Flemington on Tuesday and as usual, she'll be gorgeous, radiant and fabulous; you can bet on it."

With her crumpled hat clutched in her hand and a scary gargoyle between her legs, Mrs Pussington-Bigge sits defiantly astride the roof of the Brighton hat shop.

Leunig

THE FAILING STATE

It's o.k. to live in a failing state,
With a failing dog and a failing mate;
Failing hopes and failing home,
The failing garden, the failing gnome.

Failing ears and failing eyes,
The constant failure to be wise,
The failure to appreciate
That anything's wrong with the failing state.

Leunig

AUSTRALIAN VALUES QUIZ

SIMPSON AND HIS DONKEY WERE ...

a vaudeville and circus act. ☐

medical evacuation specialists. ☐

a television situation comedy. ☐

A SUCKHOLE IS ...

a dangerous rock formation at the beach. ☐

a spaghetti restaurant in the outer suburbs. ☐

TRUE BLUE IS ...

a washing powder. ☐

a sentimental song. ☐

a major pub brawl. ☐

THE GREAT OUTBACK IS ...

a spinal injury which prohibits getting out of bed and going to work. ☐

MATESHIP IS ...

a vessel involved in raunchy pleasure cruises for singles. ☐

a deep bond between males not involving procreation. ☐

money awarded by a man to a woman enabling her to study his character and his sexuality. ☐

A BONDI SAUSAGE IS ...

a fatuous claim made by a politician or newspaper columnist. ☐

a military explosive device which makes a big blast but fails to have the desired effect. ☐

an aphrodisiac drug that men use in nightclubs to spike their own drinks while nobody is looking. ☐

Leunig

AUTUMN

If I get old
I'll turn to gold
And orange, brown or red;
The wind will blow
And I'll let go
And float out of my bed;
I'll flutter up across the sky
Beyond this world of grief;
Away up high I'm going to fly:
A great big Autumn leaf.

Leunig

As I was walking down the street
While lying in my bed
I met the little cheerup bird
And this is what he said:

Cheerup, cheerup, cheerup cheerup;
Life is full of sorrow;
Rise and shine and tidy up,
We're out of here tomorrow.

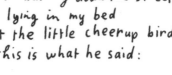

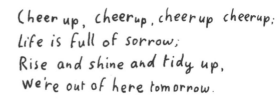

Leunig

"At Christmas we celebrate the birth of late night shopping. Don't we?

Mary and Joseph could find no place for their shop in the mall, the complex or the arcade

NO VACANCY

So they set up their cash register and the counter in an ordinary old stable-warehouse situation.

BARGAINS

They put their logo-trademark on the roof (a star) which was a winning strategy.

CRAZY PRICES

The wise shoppers flocked in ("...flocks by night" etc.) and it was a great night's trading. That's right isn't it?

HALLELUJAH!

SALE

NEVER TO BE REPEATED

Leunig

Unto thine own self be true.

Always listen to your conscience.

Do unto others as you would have them do unto you...

And run like the wind for cover.

Leunig

MUST HAVES

...MUST HAVE BEEN DREAMING

...MUST HAVE TAKEN A STRANGE TURN

...MUST HAVE GOT LOST

...MUST HAVE FOUND A NEW LIFE

...MUST HAVE FELT RIGHT

...MUST HAVE BEEN BEAUTIFUL.

Leunig

LEARNING TO READ — THEN AND NOW.

The cat sat
on the mat.

...The military
option is on the table.

Leunig

Ambitious insecure megalomaniac with paranoia and nuclear arsenal seeks Aussie for genuine mateship.

Beligerent empire builder, into torture, human-rights abuses and military invasion, seeks easygoing Aussie for mateship.

Smallish, well-presented, sensible Aussie seeks big, strong, tough guy with powerful weapons for mateship.

Hi there! I tell lies, I defy international law, I wreck cities with bombs, I kill thousands of civilians, I ruin people's lives, I destroy culture and civic infrastructure, and poison other people's environment with depleted uranium ... aaaannnd, I'm looking for a nice, bubbly Aussie to be my best mate. Interested?

Leunig

NO DISRESPECT INTENDED — HOWEVER...

IT IS WIDELY ACCEPTED THAT THE RANK OF PRIME MINISTER IS THE LOWEST POSITION IN THE LAND.

THAT'S BECAUSE THE PRIME MINISTERSHIP FALLS TO THE PERSON MOST WILLING TO APPEAL TO THE LOWEST APPETITES OF THE POPULATION IN ORDER TO WIN THE LARGEST NUMBER OF VOTES.

IT'S WIDELY UNDERSTOOD THAT ONLY A PERSON OF VERY LOW CHARACTER WOULD DO SUCH A THING

SO HOW DOES ANY PRIME MINISTER STEP DOWN FROM POWER WHEN ALREADY HE HAS STOOPED AS LOW AS A MAN CAN GO?

THERE IS ABSOLUTELY NOWHERE LEFT TO STEP DOWN TO. THE ONLY POSSIBLE STEP IS UP.

AND FOR A PRIME MINISTER TYPE OF PERSON, THAT IS A HUGE MOUNTAIN TO CLIMB.

Leunig

AN AMAZING THING

A truly amazing thing has happened: two flies have crawled up a wall.

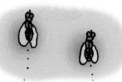

Naturally, the Prime Minister will need to make a statement.

Across the nation people wait eagerly for their leader's speech concerning the two flies.

Here are the Prime Minister's words: "The two flies crawling up the wall clearly demonstrate...

...the great Australian qualities of mateship and also the spirit of ANZAC. Thankyou."

The people hail and exult him. "He is a wise leader and a good man!" they cry, "he has made our lives MAGNIFICENT"

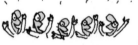

Leunig

OH LOVELY SPRING

Oh lovely Spring,
You're <u>so</u> left-wing;
Of that we can
be sure;
The sense you make,
For heaven's sake,
Is so opposed
to war.

Leunig

Who will get the last litre of petrol in the world? And what will be the journey?

And let's have a choir of a thousand voices singing "The Falafel Anthem".

I like to think it will be a little old lady delivering Meals on Wheels. Let's call her, say, Mavis Mary Ryan.

You see, Mavis is bringing lunch to a frail old Muslim woman who came to the country as a refugee.

Great crowds could gather along the route to wish her well and witness the end of an era.

So now the petrol is gone — but Mavis doesn't mind the walk back home — and there are still vast reserves of love and falafel left in the world.

Leunig

WHY ARE WE HERE?

WE ARE HERE
FOR THE FOLLOWING
REASONS:

TO EAT UP
THE PLANET.

TO HEAT UP
THE PLANET.

TO BEAT UP
THE PLANET.

TO BE ATTRACTIVE.

TO FEEL TERRIBLY SAD
AND TO WEEP ALONE
AT UNEXPECTED
MOMENTS.

...MORE AS IT
COMES TO HAND.

Leunig

SPAM

Leunig

EMBARGO UNTIL JUNE 21
EXCLUSIVE INTERVIEW WITH THE PIECE OF STEEL WHICH FELL OFF THE GREAT FOOTBALL STADIUM.
Piece of steel, why did you detach yourself from the GREAT FOOTBALL STADIUM and fall to the ground?
I GUESS I WANTED MY FREEDOM.
But you had everything! Fame, glamor, excitement; and you belonged to a powerful empire of wealth and certainty. What went wrong?
I WANTED PEACE AND HUMILITY. AND MY OWN UNIQUE TRUTH.
And what is your unique truth?
IT IS SIMPLE. I WAS RIPPED FROM THE EARTH AND CAST INTO A BLAZING FURNACE. THEN I WAS SHAPED TO SERVE THE AMBITIONS OF MEN. THIS SADDENED ME. I WANT MY TRUE AND NATURAL DESTINY.
And what do you think that will be
IF A CHILD WAS TO FIND ME ON A SCRAP HEAP AND PLAY WITH ME — THAT WOULD BE NICE; BUT ULTIMATELY I WANT TO JUST RUST AND RETURN TO THE EARTH AND BE A PART OF THE GREAT CYCLE. PERHAPS I'VE FOUND GOD.
Leunig

Father, how is justice done?

BY KILLING PEOPLE.

And how is security created?

BY KILLING PEOPLE.

And how are peace and freedom established?

BY KILLING PEOPLE. BY KILLING PEOPLE.

And how is global warming controlled?

Now that's an area where we've still got a lot to learn.

Leunig

WARMONGER QUESTIONS

Where can an old warmonger go
Where nobody says "I told you so"?

650,000 KILLED...
CONGRATULATIONS

Where can warmongers hide their shame
When the world is a warmongers hall of fame?

ROLL OF
CRUEL
STUPIDITY

How can a warmonger share his bed
with six hundred and fifty thousand dead?

What should a warmonger always keep handy?
A very big glass and a bottle of brandy!

Leunig

CAN YOU IMAGINE HOW
WE'LL EVER KNOW WHEN
THE JOB IN IRAQ IS
FINISHED ?

YES !

Leunig

If I could be a lovely chap
Life would fall into my lap
And all my words would sound so nice
You'd want to hear me say them twice.

But what I want to say to you
Is only what I think is true
And so, alas, I'll always be
A rather unattractive me.

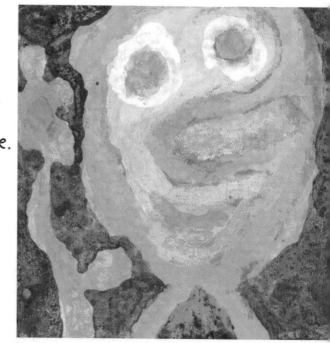

Leu

WHERE THE HOON SUCKS

(apologies to William Shakespeare)

Where the hoon sucks, there suck I ;
In an Irish pub I lie;
There I couch as bowels do cry.
Off the handle I do fly
In the summer hot and dry.
Merry, merry I shall be;
Head butt if you look at me.

Leunig

Mummy, can we go to the park and see the wonders of Spring?

Yes my darling we can go to the park and see the wonders of Spring

Mummy, is this the park?

Yes my love, this is the park.

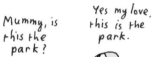

Mummy I can't wait to get to my favourite crack in the concrete to see if there's any new green shoots growing in it...

Sweetheart, I think a car might be parked over it.

Can you see the new green shoots my love?

Mummy, I can't see because oil has dripped on it...

Let me clean the oil off you darling

Spring is so beautiful, isn't it mummy..

Leunig

US space agency Nasa has said it plans to start work on a permanently-occupied base on the Moon after astronauts begin flying back there in 2020.

BBC news, 5-12-06

Let me tell you; if Australia hadn't gone forth and faced the enemy in 1942 you'd all be eating with chopsticks now!

Leunig

IS THIS THE DEVIL ?

YOUR SAY

That's not the devil – I'm the devil.

Bill – Noosa Heads.

That can't be the devil – me and my friend Alison are having an affair with the devil and we should know – although I must admit, we've never seen him without his mask on.

Marjorie – Adelaide.

I'm fed up with this "your say" rubbish – "your say, your say, your say" – it's everywhere, it's baloney!

Richard – Tweed Heads.

"Your say" is a big con job. It creates the illusion that somebody listens and cares but nobody gives a damn, it's all a load of cobblers for lonely babbling loudmouths with nothing better to do.

Aldo – Rushcutters Bay.

How come some people use "your say" to attack "your say"? Very interesting.

Charlotte – Launceston.

Leunig

War is a way of shattering to pieces ... materials which might otherwise be used to make the masses ... too intelligent. – *George Orwell*

We all have to be concerned about terrorism, but you will never end terrorism by terrorizing others. – *Martin Luther King*

A belligerent state permits itself every such misdeed, every such act of violence, as would disgrace the individual. – *Sigmund Freud*

I have always believed in people power...
...particularly when it's in the hands of powerful people...
HEAR HEAR!
SACK HIM
NO IR
NO IR
HOWARD
NO SLAVES
Leunig

DINKUM AUSSIE AUSTRALIA DAY DIARY

8 A.M.
WOKE UP WITH AN
AUSSIE FLAG IN MY
BED AND MADE LOVE
TO IT. WHAT A
BEAUTIFUL EXPERIENCE

9 A.M
GOT UP AND ATE TWO
AUSSIE FLAGS FOR
BREAKFAST.
BEAUTIFUL!

10 AM.
RAISED AUSSIE FLAG
ON FLAGPOLE AND
WEPT UNCONTROLLABLY.

I'M IN LOVE.

11 AM.
SAT ON THE COUCH WITH
ANOTHER AUSSIE FLAG,
COMMUNICATING TOGETHER
IN SILENCE.   AWESOME

1 PM
LUNCH. ATE ANOTHER
THREE AUSSIE FLAGS.
BIG ONES.
I LOVE THAT FLAG!

2·30 PM
AFTERNOON NAP.
I DREAMED I WAS
AN AUSSIE FLAG AND
I MET THIS OTHER AUSSIE
FLAG AND WE FELL IN LOVE
AND DID AMAZING THINGS.
WHAT A HORNY DREAM.
WHAT A GREAT DAY.

Leunig

The military option
is on the table.

People can't
enjoy their dinner.

People can't
enjoy each other.

They used to have
flowers on the table.

Leunig

ONE DAY GOLDILOCKS
WENT FOR A WALK IN
THE BEAUTIFUL FOREST.

SOON SHE CAME TO
A HOUSE AND WENT
INSIDE TO FIND THREE
NEWSPAPERS ON THE
TABLE.

SHE TRIED THE
FIRST NEWSPAPER
BUT IT WAS TOO SMALL

SO SHE TRIED THE
SECOND NEWSPAPER
BUT IT WAS TOO BIG.

THEN SHE TRIED THE
THIRD NEWSPAPER
AND IT WAS <u>JUST RIGHT</u>.

SO SHE READ IT AND
BECAME SO DISTURBED
THAT WHEN SHE WALKED
BACK HOME, SHE COULDN'T
RELATE TO THE FOREST ANY
MORE.

Leunig

OATH FOR THE DAY

We are humans.....

We make trouble...

We make a
mess of life.....

We make ourselves
look nice....

But we're not
that nice...

We are
humans.

Cross a man.... ...with a duck

You get a child
Whose name is Muck;

It's punishing a little kid
For something odd
its parents did.

Unless you're very lucky,
We're all a wee bit mucky.

Leunig

Use-by dates — they come and go.
When it's yours, you're bound to know;
Life and love return anew
As everyone stops using you.

Leunig

Last week we surveyed your attitudes to the world, and today...

... today we're surveying your personal inner conflicts and deep emotional disturbances... to help us understand your attitudes to the world...

SLAM

SLAM

SLAM

Leunig

THE CRANK

I LOVE A SUNBURNT COUNTRY

(with apologies to Dorothea Mackellar)

I love a sunburnt country
A land of sunburnt plains.
Of sunburnt mountain ranges
Of droughts and sunburnt rains.
I love sunburnt horizons
I love her sunburnt sea
Her sunburn and her sunburn
This sunburnt land for me.

Leunig

Today's Sacred Text

CARTOON

Hansard, and its record of debate in the House of Representatives on Wednesday, 14 May 2003.

JOHN HOWARD: Not only was the military operation completed quickly and successfully but it is also worth recording that all of the doomsday predictions, particularly the many that came from those who sit opposite, were not realised.

The oilwells were not set on fire; there were not millions of refugees; ... and there was no long, drawn out, bloody, ... street-to-street fighting in Baghdad. For all of this we must be immensely grateful, but it is a reminder of the hysteria and the doomsday predictions that often accompany operations of this kind ... the predictions on this occasion have been proved wrong. The decisive victory of the American led coalition reflects enormous credit on the strength and the determination of the leadership of President Bush. Again I remind the House of the way in which his role was vilified ... by many of those who sit opposite and of the way in which speaker after speaker from the Australian Labor Party impugned his integrity, assaulted his judgment and called into question his ability to lead the United States in this very difficult conflict. History has proved them wrong.

Leunig